Scan this barcode using your phone camera
to access the fart noises for Farting Cupid!

RULES FOR THE DON'T LAUGH CHALLENGE - FARTING CUPID

1. Don't laugh. If you do you get a point.
2. Don't smile. If you do you get a point.
3. Farting is Fine. If you do, you can deduct a point from your score.
4. Tally up the points and whoever has the fewest at the end of the book wins the highly coveted title of Fart Master!
5. Special Tie Breaker below.

In the event of a tie, there is a special bonus Tie Breaker fart button on the website that will determine who is truly the strongest willed among you all. As you read the book you may be tempted to laugh, but in order to win the game, you must do your best to keep a straight face. Farting is not only allowed but encouraged, especially in front of your parents. Everyone knows that parents love your fascination with flatulence, also known as BIG OLE FARTS.

Enjoy the game and book!

J. Cox

THE DON'T LAUGH CHALLENGE PRESENTS:

FARTING CUPID

A FART—WARMING VALENTINES STORY | CUPID BRINGS THE GIFT OF LOVE, LAUGHTER, AND FARTS TO VALENTINE'S DAY

1

He wakes up excited for what the day brings
He eats a big breakfast and stretches his wings
His stomach keeps growling he must change his diaper
This mornings breakfast turned into a quadruple wiper

He looks at the clock and there's no time to waste
He wants people to fall in love so he must move with haste
He looks in his closet for his bow, arrows, and quiver
But what he finds makes his very bones shiver

I have no more arrows, they are all gone
Can I solve this problem I've stumbled upon
I know, I'll just get more off of Amazon

He jumps in the air to take to the sky
Extending his wings and he's ready to fly
As he bursts through the clouds he begins to see
Exactly where Valentine was destined to be
An enormous Kingdom, made of pure Love
Beautiful, Brilliant, and way up above

9

Cupid spots Valentine flying with ease
"Hey...I've got a problem can you help me please!"
I've messed up like you would not believe
These arrows don't make people feel love but instead relief.
Valentine starts with a giggle and then just starts laughing
I've told you terrible news and this is how you're reacting?

10

The guy and girl start laughing so loud
Neither were awkward or angry or proud
They were apologizing and excusing
But the fart was all to amusing

They attempted some breathing
But it was hard through the wheezing
They had a smile on their face from ear to ear
Despite what had just come from their rear
"Wow, it really worked" Said Cupid with a grin
"Maybe the world has held a huge love fart in

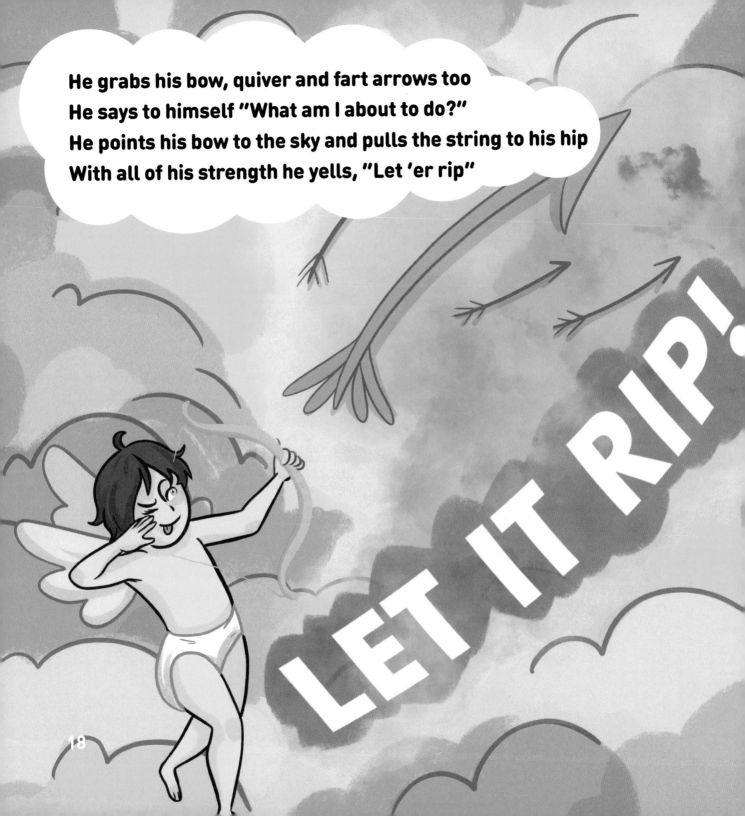

TIE BREAKER

Did you and your opponent tie?!
Here's your last chance to win!
Start a staring contest and play the TB fart.

Whoever laughs first, loses!

Made in the USA
Columbia, SC
01 February 2021

32173140R00015